I DIED

LAST NIGHT

JOHN ORR

ISBN-10: 1941972640
ISBN-13: 978-1941972649

Library of Congress Control Number: 2015937199

Published by Start2Finish Books
PO Box 680, Bowie, Texas 76230
www.start2finish.org

Printed in the United States of America

Cover Design: Josh Feit, Evangela.com

Graphic art by Stewart Yeakely. Used by permission. All rights reserved.

CONTENTS

THE INTRODUCTION

Each day, 150,000 souls are hurled into eternity. Some might pass away in a hospital or in the comfort of their own home; others might die in accidents or from any other number of ailments, happenstances, and illnesses. The fact is we all die. The real question is what comes after death?

When we die, there is an energy source that leaves the body; it is the soul leaving the mortal vessel and heading... where? Where does it go?

There are those who think it will be reincarnated, while others believe it will be absorbed into the universe. Still some say nothing at all will happen, or worse, that the soul will burn up or dissolve. If you believe in Jesus Christ, however, you know that there are only two possible destinations for your soul, should you die right now.

The story you are about to read concerns a conservative church official who died but ended up in the wrong place. Although this is a fictional account, it is based upon scriptural inferences of the eternal punishment for the wicked. You will see eternity through different lenses. The journey will be disturbing and unsettling.

Jesus is the only person who walked the earth who knew of the glories of Heaven and the despair of Hell. Luke records an event, witnessed by Christ, that reveals the rewards of the faithful soul and the devastation of the wicked. There are those who consider this event to be little more than a parable, a story, but even parables can express heavenly truths. Moreover, this is the only episode wherein Christ used a man's given name, in this case Lazarus; this detail suggests that this event actually occurred.

> There was a rich man who was clothed in purple and fine linen and who feasted sumptuously every day. And at his gate was laid a poor man named Lazarus, covered with sores, who desired to be fed with what fell from the rich man's table. Moreover, even the dogs came and licked his sores. The poor man died and was carried by the angels to Abraham's side. The rich man also died and was buried, and in Hades, being in torment, he lifted up his eyes and saw Abraham far off and Lazarus at his side. And he called out, "Father Abraham, have mercy on me, and send Lazarus to dip the end of his finger in water and cool my tongue, for I am in anguish in this flame." But Abraham said, "Child, remember that you in your lifetime received your good things, and Lazarus in like manner bad things; but now he is comforted here, and you are in

anguish. And besides all this, between us and you a great chasm has been fixed, in order that those who would pass from here to you may not be able, and none may cross from there to us." And he said, "Then I beg you, father, to send him to my father's house— for I have five brothers—so that he may warn them, lest they also come into this place of torment." But Abraham said, "They have Moses and the Prophets; let them hear them." And he said, "No, father Abraham, but if someone goes to them from the dead, they will repent." He said to him, "If they do not hear Moses and the Prophets, neither will they be convinced if someone should rise from the dead."

— Luke 16:19-31

Today, we have something better than Moses and the Law: we have the Gospel or "good news" of Jesus Christ. The Bible—both the Old and New Testaments—is about Jesus and the salvation of man. It is a handbook for the righteous, so that we do not end up like the rich man in Christ's story, destined for darkness and agony. Yet, surprisingly, Jesus also stated: "Enter by the narrow gate. For the gate is wide and the way is easy that leads to destruction, and those who enter by it are many. For the gate is narrow and the way is hard that leads to life, and those who find it are *few*" (Matt. 7:13-14).

Few! How that word haunts us all! After all, what is a few? Only eight souls were saved during the flood.[1] Only four escaped Sodom before its destruction, including Lot's wife who was turned into a pillar of salt![2] The percentage of souls saved today might be better than it once was, but God alone knows the truth. He does not want anyone to perish, for he hopes that all will come to repentance.[3]

Is there then any assurance of salvation? Can any of us be certain to reach eternity? *Yes!* As John, an apostle of Jesus, wrote, "Whoever has the Son has life; whoever does not have the Son of God does not have life. I write these things to you who believe in the name of the Son of God that you may know that you have eternal life" (1 John 5:12-13).

This is the promise of Jesus Christ, the promise of salvation and eternal glory by our Creator's side. It is a simple thing, is it not, to believe in the name of God's Son? The only thing you truly own in this life is a choice. But it is a decision that will change everything you love in life. Should you decide to go down *this* road, you will be changed forever!

After you pass from this world, after you are laid in your grave, you will never again return to the mortal realm. Consider now your own eternal destiny. Where will that one decision lead you in the end?

Where would you be if *you had died last night*?

Notes

1. Gen. 7:7; 1 Pet. 3:20
2. Gen. 19:15-16
3. 2 Pet. 3:9

THE AWAKENING

I can't breathe. I gasp and taste ash and smoke.

"Help me!"

It's so hot. Why is it so hot?

"Where am I? Help me! Help!"

I close my eyes against the heat. My flesh blisters. My lungs burn.

Hell. I'm in *Hell*! Why!? How!?

I remember now. I died last night. I died. The last moments of my life are branded into my memory. My family was beside me. My wife was sobbing; my daughter, too. The boys want to leave; they want to be anywhere but there. Were there others? Yes. They were comforting my family.

"He's in a better place now," they were saying as my soul drifted upwards.

A better place.

But I'm not! I'm *here*!

The air hurts! The smoke is filling my nostrils. I'm so

thirsty; I've never been so thirsty. Or tired. Why am I so tired!?

Please! Someone!?

I'm in agony!

Then I hear a loud voice echoing around me—or is it only in my mind? It is a whisper; it is a shout. "He will be tormented with fire and sulfur in the presence of the holy angels and in the presence of the Lamb. And the smoke of their torment goes up forever and ever, and they have no rest, day or night" (Rev. 14:10-11).

"But I don't belong here!" I cry. No one hears me though, for I am alone. There are people all around me, suffering torments and longing for the life they lost, but no one hears me. No one sees me.

I am alone among billions of desperate souls.

I begin to cry; the salty tears burn my seared, blistered skin. This is not where I thought I'd be. How did I get here? What did I do wrong?

Days have passed on earth, but time does not exist here. Not in Hell. They are having my funeral. My body is lying in an expensive casket. The preacher is trying to comfort my family. "He's still with you," he says to them.

But I'm not. I'm here.

"Maybe we'll see him in Heaven someday," my wife whispers, hopefully.

But they won't. I'm here.

"Don't listen," I scream. "There's no happy ending here!"

But they can't hear me. My voice is swallowed by the smoke and fire. I tried not to think about this ending when I was alive. I was good in life, good at keeping away from bad situations, and if I found myself between a rock and a hard place, I could get out of it again. But there's no getting out of this. There's no escape!

This is reality; my reality.

Then I hear the preacher say: "If he was here today, he would beg and plead with you to get your lives right with the Lord."

But no one is listening. They lay my dead body in the ground. My wife puts flowers on my grave. Tears are drying; hearts are already beginning to mend. My boys are just happy to be done with it all. Days turn into weeks, weeks into months. Life moves on.

But time means nothing here in the pit. In this place of torment, you relive each event over and over again. Each lash of the whip, each kiss of flame, each spear of pain: I'll feel each a thousand times over without sense of time passing. For eternity I'll linger here, but will always feel as if I had just died last night.

THE EULOGY

I can still hear the preacher talking about my life. When was it? A year ago? A week? Yesterday?

He shared that I was raised in the church. I was baptized into the church. I married in the church. At one time, I was a deacon in the church. I even attended the church where my funeral occurred. The preacher said I was a good businessman and well respected in the community. I served in the military for six years. I served on the school board. I was a community leader. I was in a travel club when I retired. I was a good provider for my family and taught my children the value of a dollar. I provided them with a good education; they grew up to have good jobs. I loved to play golf and spend time with my friends…

A few, brief sentences. This was my life. This is who I was.

The preacher concluded by comforting the mourners with a few lines from Scripture. Everyone thanked him and said he did a wonderful job; how well he had described me;

how well he must have known me.

One of my granddaughters slipped a note into my casket. "I love you, grandpa," it read in pink crayon.

Six of my friends carried my body to the graveside. One of them said, "Well, I guess he and Saint Peter are teeing up in Heaven now."

Every man ought to hear his own eulogy before he dies. In the eyes of the community, I should be in Heaven. I lived the American dream; I prospered with very few hardships. I was a good person—good to others and faithful to God.

How did I come here? I never thought this would happen to me. I'm in trouble, and there's no hope of ever getting out. I remember the sermons and lessons; it's only going to get worse after Judgment.

Why? Why am I here!? What did I do to end up here? What did I do that was so wrong?

"Why, God?" I cry out. The acrid smoke burns my throat and lungs. "Why would you send me to Hell?"

A peculiar voice answers me from the darkness. "You Englishman don't know anything," he says. "You are not in what you call Hell. Not yet."

"Who are you?" I demand.

"I am Libni of Jerusalem," replies the disembodied voice. "I lived during the time of Christ. I believed in him but was too afraid to confess him as the Son of God."[1]

"Why?"

"In my day, our livelihood depended on obeying those in charge, and they didn't believe in Jesus. Anyone who did was thrown out of the synagogue, ostracized from the community, unable to do even the simplest business in Jerusalem."

"And that is why you're in Hell?"

"I told you before," he answers, with open annoyance. "This is not Hell. 'Hell' is a place from Norse mythology; it was the underworld. Christians used this word and idea to explain the Greek 'gehenna,' which was a fiery pit, a dumping ground for our refuse, animal carcasses, and the bodies of criminals. It burned continually behind the southwest wall of Jerusalem. It was a place of carrion birds and maggots, putrid smells and a fog of smoke. Once it was a place for pagan worship where many people sacrificed their children. It was a place of abominations. It was just the place for you gentile dogs."

"For me?" I ask, balking at his absurdity. "But you're here, too."

"I know," he replies. "But we Jews were God's true people; we were not destined to this fate. Only the Gentiles—the true filth and trash of the world—were meant to linger here."

My blood boiled. *What a self-righteous hypocrite!* I thought angrily. Then I remembered telling people they would go to Hell if they didn't believe like me, if they didn't worship as I did, if they didn't live as I did. How was I any better than Libni, with his words of hate and judgment?

"You are only in Sheol, the grave," the voice continues, echoing around me. "You and I are in God's fiery pit."

"You mean, it gets worse?" I whisper.

"Yes, fool!" Libni's voice echoes. "Jesus told us how much worse it would be once we were cast into the lake of gehenna. 'If your right eye causes you to sin, tear it out and throw it away. For it is better that you lose one of your members than that your whole body be thrown into gehenna.""[2]

My eyes begin to tear; from remorse or smoke, I cannot be sure. "My right eye was greed and fear," Libni says from afar. "What was yours?"

Notes

1. John 12:42-43
2. Matt. 5:29

THE KING & I

There is silence now. Libni has left me to my fate.

It's hard to see clearly through the haze of heat and smoke. Sometimes I can see things near and far. Other times, I see only blackness.

Another voice breaks the silence, and it fills me with joy to know I am not completely alone. It also fills me with dread.

"Listen to me, my son," it calls.

"Who's there?" I reply, looking around.

The voice continues: "I have been here a long time, long before you. I may have come only yesterday or thousands of years before; it feels but a day has passed since I died."

"Who are you?" I demand again.

"Did you ever read your Bible?" he asks.

"Not as much as I should have, evidently," I reply. "I was too busy, always too much to do. Besides, I didn't understand all that 'thee' and 'thou' stuff. A lot of it was boring, just like most of the preachers I heard." Then I remember he still hasn't

THE KING & I · 19

answered me. "Now, who are you?"

"My name is Rehoboam, son of Solomon, King of Judah. I was greater than you ever imagined me to be. I had 18 wives, 60 servant wives, 28 sons, and 60 daughters."[1]

"Wow, you must have been very busy," I retort, irritated by his sense of superiority.

"Quiet, fool! I was raised in the wealthiest of nations. When I became king at 41, my father had made silver as common as stones in Jerusalem. No kingdom has ever been that wealthy or ever will be again. I had it all! I even lost over half my kingdom, plundered by the Egyptians, and still had more than I ever needed. I humbled myself and cried out, 'The Lord is righteous,' after saying and doing many foolish things. Thereafter, God strengthened my seventeen-year reign."

"So why are you here?" I ask. "I mean, you were God's anointed king. God even blessed you. What happened?"

There is a moment of grunts and cries as Rehoboam suffers torments I cannot see. "If you had read your Bible, you would know!" He spits through clenched teeth. "My life was summarized by these few words: 'And he did evil, for he did not set his heart to seek the LORD.'"[2]

A cold chill runs up my burning spine. In a way, I was just like Rehoboam. I lived in the most prosperous nation on earth and had plenty of money to live comfortably. I was never a king or in government, but in a way, I had it all. I thought that if I was a good provider, went to church regularly, and was happy, God would be pleased by my life.

Evidently, he wasn't.

Rehoboam's words, more so than Libni's, haunt my

thoughts. He did evil because he did not set his heart to seek the Lord. Did I not take God seriously enough? What else could I have done? Didn't my baptism, marriage, and being a deacon count for anything?

God, what did you want from me!?

Notes

1. 2 Chron. 11:21
2. 2 Chron. 12:14

THE DEMON

Something wet drips onto my shoulder from above, something that seers my skin. A puff of hot, putrid air ruffles my hair. I shiver, knowing there is something leering over me, something large and foul. Panic swells within me, and my mind screams at me to run—run fast and run far! But I don't move. I can't. I am enthralled by fear.

Then pain, pain like I have never known, engulfs my senses.

I scream! I scream for mercy and release! It has impaled my body, this dark creature in the shadows, thrusting sharp claws into my spine and ripping downward through muscle and sinew. O God, the pain!

For a moment, everything goes black, and I'm saved a few moments of torture. When I come to, the creature is before me, clothed in black, rotting flesh. It has the hooves of a warhorse and the tail of a scorpion. Huge black wings snap out, slick with blood and what else I dare not think about.

It circles around me, baring teeth as long as my forearm and as sharp as blades. I'm entirely at this creature's mercy, but I know there is no mercy in it. The torn flesh of my body is testament to its cruelty.

"What are you?" I whisper, my mouth filled with the metallic taste of blood. My blood.

It growls, a low guttural sound unlike any I have ever heard before. I begin to weep silently.

"For five months, I have tormented the hearts of wicked men on earth,"[1] it screeches with a voice like nails. "I was cast back into this pit, and now you'll suffer for it."

The sound of this demonic beast is unbearable; I cover

my ears to keep it out.

"What did I do?" I scream.

"You're here. That is reason enough. Our kind will torture you dogs for eternity."

"I believe in Jesus Christ!" I cry out. "I confessed Christ! Doesn't that count for something?"

"You fool," it sneers. "We also believe and tremble,[2] which is more than you ever did. I, too, confessed that Jesus was the son of the most High God.[3] I was cast out in the rebellion. But you? You had a chance to change, to make a difference, and what did you do with it? I did not receive such a chance, worthless little man."[4]

It lunges forward and, with a swipe of its tail, rips open my abdomen.

"AAAAAAAAAHHHH," I scream. "I'm sorry! Lord, forgive me! What can I do?"

Over and over again, it impales my body with tail and claw. Blood gushes from my wounds. The pain is excruciating! Just let me die! Please, God, let me die and be done with it. I don't want to exist anymore.

Why won't you let me die!?

Notes

1. Rev. 9:3-11
2. Jas. 2:4
3. Luke 8:28-29
4. Jude 6

THE RAGE

My eyes open slowly to find the creature is gone. My flesh is torn to pieces, but still I do not die. I have bled too much and too long, but still I do not die. I try to stand; I stumble. I wrap an arm around my middle to keep my organs from falling out as I try again. My legs are weak and trembling as I force them to move, to find a way out of this place.

Then I hear it, a sound more startling and eerie than the growls and screams. Laughter. I hear laughter in the darkness, followed by coughing and wheezing. It mocks me while I struggle forward until I can no longer listen to it.

"Stop," I beg. The laughter grows louder, closer. "Please," I shriek, fear turning into anger. "Stop! Let me be!"

"Well, well," a familiar voice replaces the laughter." We're all excited that you could join us, friend. Ended up like the rest of us sinners, I see. Did you become like us then? How does it feel to be a feast for maggots?"

The smell of stale, wet cigarettes hits my nostrils, making me gag. "You don't remember me, Billy Boy?" The voice is closer, but there is no one around me. "We grew up together, you and I. We went to the same school. I even partied with you, until you became too good for me. Too superior."

"Joe?" I ask, finally recognizing the voice. "Is that you?"

"It's me, all right" he replies, coughing. "I died a few years ago, and I'm not going to lie—I've been waiting for you, Billy Boy."

"Don't call me that!" I snap. I hate that name, hate who I was when he used to call me that.

"What are you going to do about it, Billy Boy?" Joe rasped through fits of coughing.

"I'll…" Do what? What can I do? I can't even see him!

Joe's laughter is manic now, triumphant. "You holier-than-thou snob! Where are your expensive clothes now? Where are your gold rings, fancy cars, and house? Where's your perfect wife? All that money that mattered so much? Where is your beloved Jesus?

"I was a good man!"

Am, I think angrily. I *am* a good man.

"When I came to your church, you told me never to come back! How Christian were you then?"

"You were drunk," I mutter, appalled. "You were embarrassing yourself."

"I was in pain, Billy Boy! Hurting, broke, homeless! Where was the charity you people preach about? Where was your kindness? I hated you then, just as I hate you now, you self-righteous hypocrite!"

I was about to explode with rage. Who was this man to judge me? I hated Joe my whole life; he was a useless drunk, an embarrassment. All he did was try to borrow money from me, which he never paid back. He always used the pet name "Billy Boy" to mock and ridicule me, to talk down to me.

"You were nothing more than a bully, Joe! A lazy, good-for-nothing waste of space! You teased and taunted me all through school!"

Joe falls silent and I think, "Good. Now you know your place."

But then he laughs, that phlegm-ridden laugh that makes me cringe. "Billy Boy, Billy Boy. I bullied you because you always acted like you were better than everyone else; we were all beneath you, to be ignored and walked over. I grew up poor and hungry; I wore the same clothes day in and day out. And how did you react? With charity? Compassion? No! You made jokes about how I smelled, about my family. You and your friends called me names! Until you needed me, of course, to get you beer underage."

"You smelled like trash; you still reek!" I yell at him, wherever he is. He laughs again, hacking and coughing as his voice fades away and is replaced by another.

"What about me? Every day you saw me and implied I was going to come here in the end, but did you ever invite me to your church? Did you ever try to save me? You never once mentioned Jesus to me!"

"Harry?" I ask quietly, not quite believing one of my old golfing buddies is here and accusing me of neglect. There is no time to say more, as more voices scream in rage and anger.

"Where were you when I needed you!"

"You cheated me out of my inheritance!"

"You ignored me as I froze on the streets! Why didn't you offer me a coat or blanket?"

"You tried to sleep with my daughter!"

"You ruined my business!"

"You never came to see me when I was in prison!"

"You never welcomed me into your church!"

"You wouldn't let me get water from your garden hose when they cut my utilities off!"

"You refused to help with my medicine!"

"You turned me away when I was homeless and starving!"

On and on, the voices shout from every direction. I failed

them, they say. I ruined their lives. All at once, my chest swells with rage until I feel I might burst. Who are they to blame me for their troubles? Who are they to claim that I am why they are here?

I struggle to take in air; each breath is hot and wet, burning my lungs. I have never felt so much anger in all my life.

"It's not my fault you suffered! It's not my fault!"

The voices grow louder, closer, pressing in on all sides of me until I crumble to my knees. I clasp my hands to my ears; it is a feeble attempt to keep their words from my brain.

"Go to Hell!" I scream. "All of you!"

Silence. Complete and utter silence.

Slowly, I lower my hands and look around. I am more alone than ever before. The voices are gone, just like the creature before them. If a pin dropped now, it would reverberate like a gong. There is no relief in the silence, though, for now I think back on my life and how I treated these poor wretches. Now I realize all the things I didn't do when alive.

I loathe myself.[1] My anger is not for them, but for me.

Notes

1. Ezek. 36:31

THE BEAST

In my agony, I still sense the presence of someone standing near, watching, and waiting. He is more evil than all who have yet visited me. In life, he was called Reverend, and millions of people listened to him, bought his books, and viewed him as a role model for the nation. But he was false. My preacher warned about these false prophets: "They are beasts with two horns of a lamb, but they speak like the dragon" (Rev. 13:11-13). He was a wolf in sheep's clothing.

I remember him because he was a household name. He mingled with dignitaries, ate with presidents, was watched by millions, and had ministries everywhere. When he spoke, tens of thousands would gather to catch a glimpse of him and hear his words. He sounded religious enough not to offend the truly faithful; he was tough on a few issues, but vague on the rest. He was the world's champion!

Now, he is here among Heaven's trash like the rest of us. He is nearby, looming in the darkness. But unlike the others, will not speak to me.

"Why me?" I cry out to him. "Why should I suffer any more than the rest of the world's filth?"

"You aren't," he replies. I can see him, but not clearly, his form misshapen behind the heat and smoke. "We all suffer here, even if you cannot see or hear or feel it. My torment is for me alone."

"But why?" I demand. "Why must we suffer so horribly?"

He is silent for a moment before quoting, "For the wrath of God is revealed from heaven against all ungodliness and unrighteousness of men, who by their unrighteousness *suppress* the truth" (Rom. 1:18).

"I was righteous! I was godly!"

"I don't know why you are being tormented," he sighs. Perhaps he has heard such weak defenses from others here. "I suppressed the truth. I couldn't have had all my wealth and popularity if I had taught everything written by the apostle Paul. Those people didn't read the Bible, and those that did listened to my interpretation. I offered them loopholes and shortcuts so as to avoid Paul's more difficult instructions.[1] All they had to do was believe, I told them, and if they worried about contradictory Bible teaching, I pulled out the 'grace' card. Grace would not only cover all sin, I taught, but would cover doctrinal error, as well.

"Had I not preached what was popular, I wouldn't have filled a single seat. If they were stupid enough to take my word as gospel and not seek the truth themselves, then they deserve to be here. I gave them what they wanted to hear, and they ate it up, hook, line, and sinker."

Then they came for him. Hundreds of thousands doomed souls fell upon him, biting and clawing him. The words, the violence, the hatred—it's too much to bear. It's like watching a mass of starving dogs tearing apart the flesh of a defenseless beast. As I watch in pity, some turn towards me, gore dripping from their claws.

"No," I whisper, shaking my head.

They charge at me, gnashing their teeth.

"No!"

They claw and bite me; ripping my flesh and breaking my bones. These are not men and women—not anymore. These are mindless beasts, governed by fear and hate.

"Why?" I cry out as they pull me down. "What did I do to you? He is the one who misled you, who suppressed the truth! He is the beast, the false teacher, not me. Please! Please, O God, stop!"

Darkness takes me. I am not out long; sleep does not come to those trapped in the pit. My body has healed, but the now fading scars still burn as if fresh. There is no sign of my attackers. But someone new is here, someone I know.

The preacher who spoke at my funeral is weeping nearby; how strange to see him here. I remember when he first came to our church and taught as the Reverend did. But our preacher wasn't so popular. In fact, many people left the church because of his teaching. Initially, what he taught had made me uncomfortable, but it fit my lifestyle. We were like the other churches around us. We became more tolerant of other beliefs and lifestyles. It was good for business.

"Didn't expect to see you here!" I call out. "What happened to all your grace?"

He doesn't answer, except to curse me. And God.

I could clearly remember the preacher as he was. It should have been obvious that he would end up here. He ran people out of church, snarled at his congregation from time to time. He told me, told us all, that we were wrong to think you had to follow the Bible literally to go to Heaven. "Even if you went to Hell," he said, "you wouldn't have to suffer eternally."

"It looks like we were all wrong," I whisper, looking around at the sea of lost faces.

There are many church leaders being tormented with us, but there is one face I don't see, one I expect to see. It is the preacher I helped run off. I hated him. He always talked about Jesus; Jesus this and Jesus that. His public speaking was not the best in the world, but he did preach his heart out—I'll give him that. He stepped on so many toes, especially when trying to help the poor and needy.

"Take from your own home," he taught. "Sell those material objects and take that money to those who need it most!"

If it were up to him, we would have given away our entire savings. How ridiculous! Every day, he grilled us about loving and forgiving one other. We weren't doing enough, he scolded, to save the lost in our community, to defend them from the many "beasts" or false teachers. He spent so much time with drug addicts and the poor that there was little left for us, the pillars of the church. He wore us out!

Finally, we had had enough. The church was split about firing him, but it didn't matter in the end. He said he wouldn't be the cause of a division and that it was clearly time for him to go. I was never so happy to see anyone leave!

I look around me now, through smoke and heat, at the many false prophets who led so many astray. Still, I do not see that one man, the one I helped cast out. I want to ask why he isn't here with the rest of us, why he isn't here suffering!

But I already know why. I know.

Notes

1. 2 Pet. 3:15-16

THE LIGHT

I't's so dark. It weighs down on me, pressing against my chest until I can barely breathe. The darkness hides the creatures that torment me, but it cannot hide my thoughts. Instead, it magnifies them, conjuring memories of guilt and shame until I begin to weep.

I'm terrified of this darkness!

I try to think of the good things in my life because such thoughts bring a sliver of light to my unending nightmare. My mama is the first person that comes to mind. What a wonderful human being. Whenever I needed some good news or encouragement, I knew I could talk to her, and she would cheer me up. I wish so desperately I could see her again. Just one word from her, one glance of her sweet smile would lighten up my entire miserable existence.

Mama wasn't always that way. When she met my father, she was a wild child. Young and naïve, she fell for his charm like so many other women before and after. I know she regretted some of her decisions, but she was loyal and good, even when my father was not.

At one of her lowest moments, she wanted to kill him while he slept. She had taken too much abuse, too much betrayal from that alcoholic womanizer. But she didn't. She saw me asleep that night and knew she couldn't do it. She confessed this to me when I had grown up and explained that her life was nothing when compared to her family.

Was she right? I don't know, but I respected and loved her every day of my life because of her strength.

The day after she chose not to kill him, her friend invited her to church. So she went and went again; she took my sister and me as well. Eventually, she was baptized. I'll never forget how happy she was that day or how angry it made Dad.

"If you go to that @#$% church one more time, I'll kill you!" he screamed one Sunday as Mama led us to the door. He was drunk again, eyes bloodshot and wild. "Go ahead. See if I don't!"

She tucked us behind her as she faced him. "After thirteen years, I found something to live for, someone who loves me more than you ever could. If you pull the trigger, I'll go to Heaven. If you don't, I'll go to church. Either way, I'll be with the One who really loves me."

"No one loves you," my dad spat, drool literally dripping down his chin.

"Jesus does," she replied calmly. I remember she started to cry then, even as she smiled. "Come on, kids. Let's go."

Dad didn't stay around long after that, but that was all right. When he left, so did his cruelty and hate. We were dirt poor, but we managed all right. And Mama's faith continued to grow. She devoted her life to the Lord and his good news. I remember being in her Sunday school class when I was in the fourth grade, and she made us memorize the presentation of the gospel. I still remember it. She drilled the Scriptures into our heads on how to be saved.

"You must *desire* the gospel," she told us, "as explained in 1 Tim. 1:15-16. But you must also *believe* in the gospel[1]," she would add. "And when you desire the gospel in order to believe in it fully in your heart, then you must seek to *understand* the gospel.[2] You must then *confess* the gospel, as told to us in Acts 8:36-37," she said then, the pattern of salvation becoming clear.

"Like when we confess our sins?" one of us asked, hand raised in the air. Mama smiled; I remember her smile.

"In a way, but instead of sins or guilt, we are acknowledging Jesus as the Christ and Son of God. And by doing that, you are declaring your undying love for him. Understanding the gospel and recognizing Jesus Christ as our Savior, is not enough, though. You must also *obey* the gospel.[3] Does anyone remember the last step?"

Blank faces were all that replied. We always struggled with this last element, although I don't know why.

"You must *live* the gospel," Mama answered for us. "Each and every day, you must love Christ with all your heart and obey his teachings."[4]

Mama worked so hard to make sure all of her students not only memorized these Scriptures, but understood what they meant. Blind faith wasn't enough; we needed to appreciate the importance of the gospel in our paths to salvation.

My sister did understand the gospel. She was always inviting people to church and bringing them to the Lord. I think she brought more people to Christ than the elders and preachers did. She was so sweet; it made me sick.

She started bringing people over to our house to study the Bible. It angered me; I thought she was a fanatic. Sometimes I would tease her by calling her "Mama's clone." Later, she married a preacher. Big surprise, right? They decided to be missionaries in Africa. Mama was so proud of her, so proud. It made me jealous. What was I, chopped liver? Wasn't I just as important? Mama would smile and tell me she loved me, that she loved us both equally. But I always suspected she loved my sister just a little bit more.

My sister had been in Africa several years when she died. By then, she had two children of her own and had begun taking on extra work. She taught children in a small, predominately Muslim village, but was making inroads into the community. A few locals had also become Christians thanks to my sister's joy in Christ. She loved the children she taught, loved her faith, and loved her life.

I heard about it two days after she died. Mama called me; I could barely understand her. One of my sister's students, a little girl, had set her backpack by her desk, so my sister asked her to move it out of the aisle and put it in her cubby. The girl refused. When my sister finally picked the bag up to put it away. Apparently, the little girl began screaming that my sister had taken the girl's Koran. Other children began telling their families that my sister was forcing them to be Christian and forsake Allah.

They came for my sister soon after that, a group of men led by the local imam. They took her from the schoolhouse and shot her in front of her students. Not long after that, they killed my brother-in-law, my niece, and my nephew. They burned their bodies in the street over a misunderstanding.

After we received the news, something died inside Mama and me. She consoled herself like any mother who had lost her child on the battlefield would—through tears and anger, depression and, finally, acceptance. Mama said my sister and her family had given their lives for the Lord; they were heroes working towards something bigger than themselves. Mama was proud—sad, but proud.

I, on the other hand, grew bitter. I blamed all Muslims for what happened to my sister, rather than focusing on the few actually responsible. I blamed my brother-in-law for dragging her to a third-world country. Most of all, I blamed God. Why would he do that to someone who loved him that much? I resigned from being a deacon. I stopped going to church regularly. Sometimes Mama and I would just hold each other and cry, but she would always say, "Don't worry, son. We'll see her again soon."

Whenever she said that, I would think, "There's nothing beyond this. There's nothing for us after death."

I was wrong. So very, very wrong.

Mama was diagnosed with cancer a few years after my sister died. It was aggressive and took her quickly. But she was never sad. When she shared her test results, she smiled—actually smiled—and said, "I'm going home."

They were rough, those last few months. She was in so much pain and taking so much medication. We tried to make her comfortable; we brought in hospice and transferred her to a hospital facility that gave her 100% care. I remember one night I sat with her, holding her hand in mine, hating how frail she had become, hating that she was going to leave me.

"Don't be angry, son. Don't hold onto your bitterness," she said softly. "I love you," she added with a sigh before closing her eyes. "Your sister and I will be waiting for you."

She died a few hours later.

Then I became even angrier with God. I hated him, doubted him, cursed his name.

"Why, God?" I call out into the flames and smoke-laden air. "Why did you have to take my sister and my mother? Why would you do that to someone who loved you with all their heart and soul? Why have you hurt me so much? What did I ever do to you? Why did you take Mama from me?"

I weep; the tears burn my maimed flesh. I fall to my knees in helpless agony and cry uncontrollably.

"Please, God. Please help me! Help me see the light," I whimper. "Help me see it?"

Notes

1. 1 Cor. 15:1-4
2. Rom. 6:3-7
3. Acts 2:37-39
4. Gal. 2:20

THE PLEA

It seems like I have been here for years, yet the only vivid memory I have is of dying last night. The heat and my own thirst are overwhelming. Finally, I turn my attention away from the horror around me to a place that feels farther away than ever. I struggle to visualize it.

"Hello," I ask. "Is anyone there who will listen to me?"

I look to what Jesus called "Paradise" and, although I don't know how, I see beyond this great chasm of torment and despair. I see something so beautiful, so unlike anything I ever witnessed on earth, that I cannot describe it. Simply looking upon it could calm the most troubled of hearts. Just the thought of it relieves a little of my torment and pain, but even this reprieve is immediately overtaken by intense sorrow.

I should have been *there*—not *here*!

I cry out again, "Help me! Somebody answer me, please!"

In that beautiful place, I catch a glimpse of a woman I knew when I was a police officer, a prostitute whom I had once escorted from the county jail for syphilis treatments. Years later, I saw her walk down the aisle at church with her old, raggedy sister for baptism. As they walked forward, someone overheard me saying, "What are they doing in here?"

I was criticized for those words, but I knew what that woman was. I had gone to that church most of my life, put money in the collection plate, and was a good, law-abiding citizen. I never went to jail. I was never treated for a sexually transmitted disease. My taxes had provided welfare checks for that woman and others like her. But she is in paradise while I rot down here!? The least she could do is bring me some water, something to ease this torment.

"Hey!" I call, trying to get her attention. "Help me! I'm miserable down here!"

Another figure looks my way, someone I have never seen before, yet know instantly. He is the apostle John. Surely he will offer me his hand and drag me out of the pit!

"John," I plead with a wheezing cough. "Have mercy on me. Make that skank bring me some water. I waited on her enough in life; it is her turn to return the favor."

"Son," he replies, "remember that in your life you were blessed beyond measure, while this poor woman suffered. She did everything she could to feed her family, including selling herself. But later in life, she found Jesus and embraced his love and forgiveness with all her heart. Now she is comforted, while you are tormented."[1]

I don't believe it. Was I blind to the hardness of my own heart? Was I so evil that I was worse than her? Then an image of my own daughter, still alive on earth, formed before me.

She was looking at herself in a mirror. She's so beautiful, I think, so alive and pure. But then I see deeper, her very soul laid bare to me. There is nothing there but death.

"Apostle John," I scream, "please send that old prostitute to warn my daughter. She's going to end up here with me unless someone warns her! What about my wife and two boys and their families? I know their hearts are not right with Jesus; he was just a story they grew up with. It wasn't real to me either, not like it should have been. I didn't give them the right priorities. I emphasized jobs and sports and making money ahead of God. Somebody has to do something. *Please!*"

"Son," John replies, "they have the gospel of Christ. I see four or five Bibles sitting around them. Let them hunger for spiritual food instead of a consumption of things.

"But sir," I beg, "if someone came back from the dead, they would repent."

John said to me, before vanishing from my sight: "If they won't listen to Jesus and his words, they will not be persuaded by someone else who comes back from the dead."

I cannot bear the thought of them ending up here with me. All I can think about was the last time I saw them as they sat around my deathbed.

"You're going home. We'll see you again someday."

But this place isn't what we had in mind.

None of this was.

Notes

1. Luke 16:25

THE WEEPING &
GNASHING OF TEETH

It's so hot here; so painful.

It still feels as though I just died last night, but I don't know how long I've been here already. I can hear angry voices, millions of souls blaming, cursing, crying, and screaming. I can see the demons, the torment, and the horror of what is going on around me; the fiery worms bursting through charred remains, the destruction of the body before it is re-animated for more suffering, more torment, and an eternity dying, yet no death.

Imagine having your flesh ripped to pieces by some sadistic serial killer. Imagine the pain and horror of watching him take delight in every scream as you beg for your life. Eventually, it doesn't matter anymore. You just want him to get it over with and let you die. You can see your mangled body and the ghastly scene left by the killer, but only for an instant. Then suddenly, you wake up, whole once again, before he starts to dissect you all over again. And again. And again.

Maybe this time he pours gasoline all over you and sets you on fire. The next time he beats you with a blunt object. Or maybe he throws you into an open grave and buries you alive. Each time can be different and worse than the time before. Multiply that pain and terror by a thousand and you will begin to understand what I go through continually and without rest.

I'm so tired. I want to die. I've even tried taking my own life, but I just keep coming back.

"Will it ever end? Haven't I suffered enough?"

The moaning and groaning of all the people around begins to echo and resound in my head until it is all I can hear...

"Why did God put me here?"

"Where am I?"

"It's not my fault."

"No one ever told me about this place."

"I never felt welcome in that church."

"It's that preacher's fault!"

"It's my parents' fault!"

"It's my husband's fault!"

"It's the priest's fault!"

"It's Adam and Eve's fault!"

"It's the devil's fault!"

"I was told I'd have sex with 70 virgins for an eternity."

"I never had time for God!"

"I never read the Bible."

"I never had a Bible."

"I couldn't overcome my addiction."

"God never loved me."

"Christians always judged people."

"I thought everyone would go to Heaven."

"I thought this Hell stuff was made up."

"I could never accept a God who lets people suffer."

"I thought, when I died, I'd be re-incarnated into someone else."

"I didn't believe I had to go to church to be saved."

"I thought one church was as good as another."

"I thought one religion was as good as another."

"I thought one God was as good as another."

"I didn't agree with everything in the Bible."

"I thought Hell was on earth."

"I didn't need religion as long as I had liquor."

"I devoted my life to exterminating religion."

"I thought the apostle Paul was prejudiced against women."

"I felt God asked too much of me."

"I believed the television preachers. I gave thousands to them, so God would bless me. Why am I here?"

"I thought Jesus was for hicks and rednecks—you know, uneducated people."

"I left the church because it was too boring."

"I quit the church because someone hurt my feelings."

"No one was able to heal me; they said I didn't have enough faith."

"I accepted Jesus as my personal Savior; what happened?"

"I cut out verses in the Bible I didn't agree with."

"I didn't know I was doing anything wrong."

"I was a good person on earth; I deserve better than this!"

And on and on and on. You wouldn't believe the moaning and complaining and whining. Some people weep over their decisions in life, while others gnash or grind their teeth in anger. I cannot take it anymore and begin to scream, hands clasping my mangled ears.

A voice breaks through the torment. It is familiar, so agonizingly familiar.

"Daddy?"

My daughter. Dear God, not her. Not my child.

She is different now, not my beautiful little girl anymore. She is haggard, old, and tired; ugly and monstrous. Had so much time elapsed on earth? Had I been here that long?

"Baby," I weep, "I'm so sorry you are here. I tried to send help, but no one would warn you; no one would help me save you."

"Why didn't you take Jesus seriously?" she cries out, angrily. "We all thought you would be in Heaven when you died, because you lived such a good life. So we followed your example. But my life became one disappointment and heartache after another, all because of you!"

She turned to leave, but I call after her: "Where are your brothers? Where are your mother and my grandchildren?"

The creature that was once my daughter whips around, spittle dripping from her rotting mouth. "They hate you," she shrieks. "*We all hate you!* They never want to speak to you again."

I feel worthless and so very alone as my precious daughter leaves me. Nothing hurts worse than my child's words of hate and scorn. My own family hates me, just as I hated my father for what he did to my mother and sister. Truly this is the worst punishment of all.

Then something dawned on me. Everything she said, every complaint from the billions of people trapped in the pit revolved around a single word: *I.*

I feel. I think. I believe.

In all my time here, I have never heard anyone speak of what *Jesus* thought, what *Jesus* believed, or what *Jesus* felt. Perhaps that is why we are all here, suffering torment and pain for eternity, instead of being over yonder.

I remember a song we sang a lot in church:

"When the roll is called up yonder, I'll be there."

My friends and I would change it up and say, "When the roll is called up yonder, you'll be there," while pointing downward, mocking those trapped in Hell. But now, it's not so funny. Somewhere along the way, my name was removed from the Book of Life. I didn't just die last night; I died a long time ago. Jesus was important to me, but not important enough for me to seek him with all my heart and soul. I can still recall those words said about king Rehoboam: "He did evil, for he did not set his heart to seek the LORD" (2 Chron. 12:14).

I knew very few people in life who were that serious about Jesus. I rarely heard his name mentioned in public unless it was used as a by-word. Every time I look back to my life, I begin thinking about my desires. I enjoyed the world and making money, even if I cheated and lied. I loved golf. I loved my family, but seldom had time for them. I was a proud man who sought notoriety, wealth, comfort, and respect. I read many books and was well educated; I prided myself on knowing many things. I had opinions for everything. But I never really set my heart on seeking the Lord. I just went to church to escape Hell.

O God, I understand now! You weren't just talking about Rehoboam! You were also talking about *me*!

THE MISSING

There are times I can reflect on my life despite the constant pain, but it only makes my suffering worse. It occurred to me one day—or night, I cannot be sure—everything that was missing from this new existence.

There is no color here, unless grey, black, and a perpetual gloom excite you. Everything God created for us to enjoy does not exist in the pit. Everything good is missing. No one parties. Drugs, alcohol, pills: things people use in life to numb pain are absent. The vices that allowed many of these souls to escape from reality cannot help them anymore.

How I long for a drink of cool water or the simple ability to breathe fresh air! I remember how I enjoyed fishing: the smell of the lake and trees, the feel of the boat gently rocking on the water, the cool breeze, and the sunshine all around me. Then there was the thrill of catching a fish and the excitement of bringing home the catch of the day. The stories and friendships born from those simple moments are gone.

The smell of a family barbeque, the taste of burgers and fries, and the anticipation of a home-cooked meal have been replaced by the stench of smoke and burning flesh. Now, instead of sating my appetite, I want to vomit. Instead of relaxation, I am constantly exhausted. Instead of joy, there is pain—horrible pain and suffering.

Holidays, birthdays, and anniversaries mean nothing here. Feelings of great anticipation are replaced by emptiness. Someone once said, "You can live a month without food, three days without water, and three minutes without air; but you can't live three seconds without hope."

There is no hope down here. We suffer and bleed over and over again. I wish to God we could die.

Here, our bodies and souls are exposed for everyone to see and judge. I used to eagerly look at images of naked women for my own pleasure. Here, however, we are all bare and it is the foulest, ugliest sight. We are wrapped in shame and self-loathing with nothing to hide ourselves behind. Every inch of us is laid bare for ridicule and torture. Our wounds are never bound, our depression and anxieties untreated.

What I wouldn't give to feel something besides pain and torture! Another human's touch or a child's embrace, encouragement and laughter, compassion, forgiveness, respect, innocence, excitement! A kiss or a hug… All those warm and fuzzy feelings are missing down here. So, too, is everything good, wholesome, and valuable. There are no children here. Nothing that reminds us of what "good" actually is.

Not missing are most of the world's leaders, kings, and financial giants; philosophers, preachers, and professors; actors and hypocrites. Those who thought they ran the world, the church, or industry are well represented in the pit. We idolized them all in life, mimicking and judging their every move. We worshipped them.

As I see all these important people imprisoned alongside the most ordinary sinners, I am reminded of something Mama always said to me: "For what does it profit a man to gain the whole world and forfeit his soul? For what can a man give in return for his soul?" (Mark 8:36-37).

I thought I could have it both ways. How wrong I was!

I miss so many things. Simple things I took for granted: a smile, the ability to sleep and dream, to eat and drink, go where I want to go, do what I want to do. I miss my freedom! The worst prison on earth is nothing compared to this. There was a prison ministry at the church I attended, but I never wanted to participate; who wants to be around that kind of scum? They had it too easy in prison. Why bother trying to send a preacher to save their miserable souls?

I wish someone would come to save our souls now. The only preaching anyone receives down here is about our doom.[1]

Everything good and enjoyable in life is missing here. All that is left is filth, sadness, and fear. Most of all, there is regret. Regret for what was done in life, but also for what we failed to do. I just wish I, too, was missing from this place!

Notes

1. 1 Pet. 3:19

THE HAPPENING

All at once, there is a great noise, both deep and deafening. The ground shakes, and rocks fall from above. Everyone begins to run. Some people are trampled in the madness; some are crushed by debris. We all know something horrible is about to happen. Chills run along my spine, an omen of things to come.

Then the earth's sky is ripped away, and people everywhere begin to burn. Below, we wished the rocks and mountains of earth would fall upon us and spare us the cremation of the living.[1] Nothing, however, drowns out the screaming of the condemned. Paradise is being emptied.[2]

Not all are destroyed. Some are rising into the air to meet Jesus. The worthy are stretching forth their hands to join the Lord.[3] Few are their numbers; so few.

All at once, the earth, stars, and planets explode. The galaxies begin to collapse into themselves—billions of them, blinking out of existence; fire and destruction are everywhere.

Finally, the universe returns to what it originally was: *nothing*![4]

Suddenly, we are transported to a place worse than our previous prison. We stand before a great white throne,[5] and the light before our eyes blinds us with excruciating pain. We were bound in darkness for so long that we cannot bear to look upon the light. As my eyes adjust, an unbelievable scene is set before me. I cannot describe it with words, for it is goodness personified.

All God's saints are being escorted before the great throne, not to be judged, but to be glorified by God. It is similar to the sun shining on the moon at night; the moon has no glory in and of itself, but receives its splendor from the sun. The saints are humble and pure, bowing before their King's brilliance.

I now realize that the street of gold and pearly gates are not references to a place, but rather to the people of God.[6] In shame, I hide before the sight like a beggar cowering in the darkness. How I want to be with them, kneeling at God's feet.

I could have been with them. I could have been among the holy few, but the old world and its temptations were more important. I hang my head in despair.

Then Jesus appeared. All of us bowed and confessed Jesus Christ as Lord.[7] Many begin to whisper that this is it! Jesus will save us now that we have learned the error of our ways. The rest of us, however, knew something worse lay ahead. Everyone trembles with fear for no one knows what to expect next. In desperation, we declare that Jesus is Lord. Again and again, we shout this one truth until the emptiness is filled with our voices. We blind ourselves with hope of redemption, but it does not come. Instead, we face our final judgment.

Our cries of faith and hope are silenced as each and every one of our sins is displayed before our eyes. We are being judged by the deeds, or lack thereof, we committed in our lives.[8] All of us must account for every careless word that came from our mouths, as well as every thought born in our wicked hearts.[9]

I don't know how, but we see every wicked thought and deed of every person as quickly as a flash of light, though it feels like an eternity. It is the most embarrassing, repulsive, and disgusting experience I have ever had. I want to die, to bury myself in a hole and forget what I have just seen. Why would God let everyone see every glance, every thought, every lie, and every sin?

I hid so many things in life, keeping so much secret to avoid embarrassment or shame. Others also kept quiet about the awful things I did. I blamed everyone else for my missteps and thought, if things remained hidden, I had gotten away with it. But I didn't. I believed I lived a good enough life to go to Heaven, but I didn't.

Seeing my own crimes written across the sky horrified me, but then I saw my wife and children's sins. How could they? How could they do such terrible things? Then I see what my friends thought of me, what they said behind my back. How could my closest friends, the people who knew me best, think so low of me?

We are not alone in our sins. Even the most revered, "saintly" people in history were no better than the rest of us. Most of my heroes were nothing but trash, hiding behind fictional façades of righteousness. They are all liars and sinners!

All of them! Only those who loved the Lord with all their heart and soul escaped this grand spectacle of humiliation.

With an expression of anger and sadness, Jesus speaks to me now that the images have passed. "I know your works: you are neither cold nor hot. Would that you were either cold or hot! So, because you are lukewarm, and neither hot nor cold, I will spit you out of my mouth. For you say, I am rich, I have prospered, and I need nothing, not realizing that you are wretched, pitiable, poor, blind, and naked.[10]

"You knew the truth, but kept it from others. You knew well the ways of the world. You wanted to be a successful businessman. I gave you that success, but you never wanted to know me. You owned 43 Bibles in your lifetime but seldom searched for spiritual nourishment. When you were not fruitful in my kingdom, I begged my Father to give you more time. He eventually said, 'Cut him off. He's just filling a seat.'"[11]

"But Lord," I beg, "didn't I serve the church as a deacon? Didn't I work at the local food pantry? You know I wasn't good at saving souls. I even admit that I wasn't easy to get along with, but am I as bad as these others who killed millions of your people?"

He replies, "I never knew you; depart from me, you workers of lawlessness."[12]

"But Lord Jesus, why am I suffering more than others?"

He does not respond immediately, and I feel the weight of his silence crushing down upon me. Finally, he speaks to me.

"You knew what was required of you. You were raised by a godly mother, yet you did not take me seriously. Your righteousness never exceeded the Pharisees of my day.[13] There are billions of souls wishing they had heard all that you were taught. I tell you it will be better for the inhabitants of Sodom and Gomorrah than it will be for you."[14]

"But why, Lord? Why?" I whisper in terror.

"Son, to whom much is given, from him much will be required. To you whom much has been entrusted, I expected so much more."[15]

Notes

1. Rev. 6:16
2. 1 Pet. 3:18
3. 1 Thess. 4:13-17
4. 2 Pet. 3:10-13
5. Rev. 20:11-15
6. Rev. 21:9-27
7. Phil. 2:10-11
8. Rev. 20:12
9. Matt. 12:36
10. Rev. 3:15-17
11. Luke 13:6-9
12. Matt. 7:23
13. Matt. 5:20
14. Mark 6:11
15. Luke 12:47-48

THE BEGINNING
OF THE END

His words hurt more than all the other torments I had yet experienced. It is the kind of hurt that strikes deep inside and twists like a thousand knives. Those are the words I will take with me to my final torment for all eternity.

If only I could go back to the night before I died. I would have made a plea so terrifying, so heart-rending, that someone would have listened. I know now that I deserve to be here, but maybe I could have saved my family from this awful fate.

I remember that night so clearly. I wanted to say something, but I was in such pain that all else seemed unimportant. I didn't know what pain was then. I should have said something. I wish to God my dying breath had been, "Save yourselves."

"Lord," I cry out. "You can do anything. Give me a chance to live my life again. Let me have another opportunity. This time, I will love you with *all* my heart and soul. Nothing will stop me from doing your will. *I will tell everyone about you*."

Silence is the only response to my prayer.

"Please," I whisper. "Let me at least go back to my last night on earth. Let me look into my daughter's tearful face and tell her I was wrong. Let me tell my sons not to make the same mistakes I did. Let me tell my wife how sorry I am. Let me…"

Suddenly, two of God's angels are coming toward me. They aren't little babies with wings or beautiful women; the artists were all wrong. They are war-like, frightful creatures. They remind me with voices that deafen the ears, "It is appointed for man to die once, and after that comes judgment."[1]

They are not merciful. They are deaf to my pleas and screams. Together, they lift me and cast me toward a maelstrom of fire and darkness.[2] It is an ocean of damned souls burning, screaming, and suffocating for all eternity. I would have given my right eye to have known this was going to happen. What changes I would have made to my life if I knew that this awaited me!

There is no bottom in this storm of souls. I keep falling toward my final doom, unable to pull air into my lungs or settling the roiling of my stomach. "O God, I could never have imagined something worse than the place of torments!"

I can't stop screaming and crying. Fear and anxiety are exploding within me. As I penetrate through the darkness, I am met by blue-hot flames I cannot see, but that burn my very soul. I am drowning in my pain, suffocated by invisible, acrid smoke.

"Why, God? Why must I suffer such torture?"

There is no end, however, to this torment. I burn but never die. I suffocate but cannot stop screaming. Don't ask me how, for I can't explain this horror. Worms and maggots wriggle in and out of my charred remains. It is the most horrible, frightening dream from which I can't awake.

I just keep falling without rest. I'll never hit bottom.

The pain will never dull.

My lungs will never fill.

It will never stop, and I will never get out of here.

And as I fall, demons reach forth and torture my mind and flesh. Demons, worse than any I met in the pit, bite and gouge and stab as I fall down, down, down.

Wasn't this place prepared for *them*? Isn't this their prison? Why am *I* here among them!? Will it ever end?

Amid the pain, a memory of the young preacher I hated rises in my thoughts. He kept warning us by quoting this passage over and over again: "Depart from me, you cursed, into the eternal fire prepared for the devil and his angels" (Matt. 25:41).

I hate that the young preacher was right. I hate God for putting me here. I hate the devil for lying to me. I hate everyone. I hope all men, women, and children have to suffer just like me. I hate that I was ever born. I hate my old man; how I hope he is being punished ten-fold. I hope every smooth-talking preacher and religious leader is writhing in unimaginable agony. I really hope Joe is a buffet for worms right now.

I want my mother. O God! I wish I was with her. I wish she could wake me up from this awful nightmare, hold me in her sweet arms, and promise nothing bad will ever happen.

"Make it stop, Mama!" I try to scream these words, but they come out strangled and weak. "Please, God, I'm so sorry. Please let me see Mama just one more time. Let her hold my hand again and take me to church. I would love to hear her reading the Bible before she tucks me in at night. When I hurt or got in trouble, she would always make it right. Please, Mama, I'm in so much trouble. I'll memorize more Scripture for you. I want to hear your sweet voice again. I'm so afraid and alone. I'm in so much pain. Please help me, Mama! Pleeeeeeeease!"

The truth is that I'll never see my mother or sister again. I'll never see anyone good again. I wasted all my opportunities and threw away the grace of God. I wasted my life. Only now I realize the most important love in a man's life is his God, his Creator. God, the Father who breathed into my body the breath of life, a part of himself. The one that loved us so much that he gave his only begotten Son.[3] If only I had loved God as much as I loved my mama, my family. I loved playing golf more than I loved the one who died in my place.

O God… O God… O God!

Wait. What is that falling toward me? It's massive and coming towards me like a bullet. Its face… its face is horrifying. It is mangled and putrid, covered in oozing pustules while its mouth spews fire. My eardrums burst and my nose bleeds. My heart is beating so fast it is about to explode!

O God, what is that smell? It's so strong I can taste it; bile

rises into my throat.

Everything is so dark… so smoky… but the demon is crystal clear. Everything is moving so fast, yet slow, all at the same time.

And then I realize this is no ordinary demon. This is him… Satan! The great dragon of old.[4] The one who hated me in life almost as much as God loved me. And now he's coming straight toward me.

The creature's jaw gapes open as it approaches, revealing the fragments of its recent victims. It drips gore and reeks of death.

It is coming closer and closer, moving faster and faster…

No, God! NO!!

NOOOOOOOOOOOOO!!!!!!!

Help me.

Notes

1. Heb. 9:27
2. Matt. 5:29-30
3. John 3:16
4. Rev. 20:2

THE CONCLUSION

Seek the LORD while he may be found; call upon him while he is near; let the wicked forsake his way, and the unrighteous man his thoughts; let him return to the LORD, that he may have compassion on him, and to our God, for he will abundantly pardon. For my thoughts are not your thoughts, neither are your ways my ways, declares the LORD. For as the heavens are higher than the earth, so are my ways higher than your ways and my thoughts than your thoughts. For as the rain and the snow come down from heaven and do not return there but water the earth, making it bring forth and sprout, giving seed to the sower and bread to the eater, so shall my word be that goes out from my mouth; it shall not return to me empty, but it shall accomplish that which I purpose, and shall succeed in the thing for which I sent it.

— Isa. 55:6-11

Someone once said, "It was easier when I thought believing in Jesus and keeping the Ten Commandments would ensure my salvation. Then I began studying the Bible, and my world turned upside down."

The greatest treasure we have on earth is not made of silver and gold. It is the truth of God's Word, and God's Word is Jesus (John 1:1). Men and women, educated and uneducated, have tried to disprove the Bible, argue against God, and discredit Jesus. However, there is no other reliable core of truth. All else is from man.

We cannot find reality in this life but beyond the grave. Your soul lives inside a human body temporarily. You must set your heart to seek the Lord today, not tomorrow. If you love him with all your heart and soul, then your greatest desire will be to believe and obey him. As you continue to study the Bible, you will learn what you must do in order to be saved. If you choose to listen to the religious leaders of the world, you'll hear one thing; if you search God's Word, you'll do another. As someone once said, "It is easier to believe a lie you've heard a thousand times, than to believe the truth you've only heard once."

Remember, if you do what they did in the first-century church, you can achieve the triumphs they achieved. You, too, can be one of the few who have dedicated themselves solely to the Lord and be saved. God will help you if you begin now to "setting your heart to seek the Lord." Ask God to help you find the truth about Jesus, salvation and his kingdom. Tell him you don't want to be deceived by false teachers.

Study his Word; start with Genesis or Matthew and read

at least a chapter each day. When interpreting Scripture, always read each section in its entirety; understand the context of the passage. In this way, his Word will begin to change your life. If you commit to seeking God with your whole heart, your life will change completely and only for the better. You will be amazed at where your journey with Jesus will take you.

In Luke 10:25-28, a lawyer asked Jesus: "'Teacher, what shall I do to inherit eternal life?' He said to him, 'What is written in the Law? How do you read it?' And he answered, 'You shall love the Lord your God with all your heart and with all your soul and with all your strength and with all your mind, and your neighbor as yourself.' And he said to him, 'You have answered correctly; do this, and you will live.'"

Jesus loves you with all his heart and soul. Why else did he die for you? If you want to live forever, you must learn to trust and obey him.

Most importantly, do not put off your spiritual education for some future time. Consider the Scriptures used in this book as a wake-up call from the Lord. After all, you may never get this opportunity again. Reflect upon these words from Heb. 3:14-15: "For we have come to share in Christ, if indeed we hold our original confidence firm to the end. As it is said, 'Today, if you hear his voice, do not harden your hearts...'"

Ask yourself each and every day this one question, for it may be the most important question of your life:

Where you would be if you died last night?